Learn to read with

Fat Cat

Words by Sue Graves
Illustrations by Jan Smith

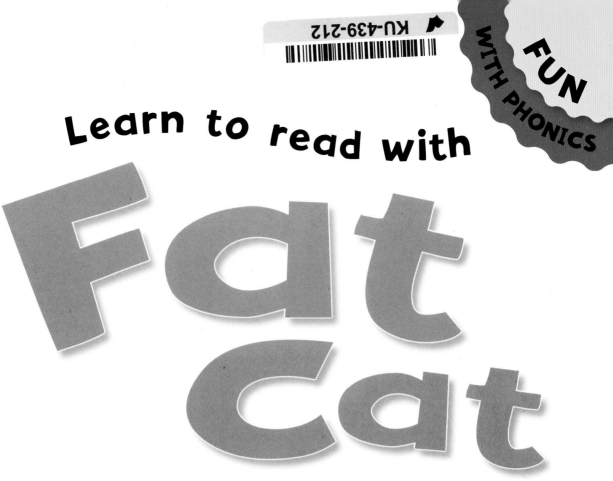

Fat Cat is Pat's cat.

'Hello Fat Cat.'

He sleeps all day on his warm mat.

One day Pat saw a rat in her hat.

'Get that rat',
said Pat.
'Get that rat!'

But Fat Cat
just sat...
and sat!

But she tripped
and fell over
Fat Cat's mat.

'Now Fat Cat's a flat cat!' laughed the rat.

The end